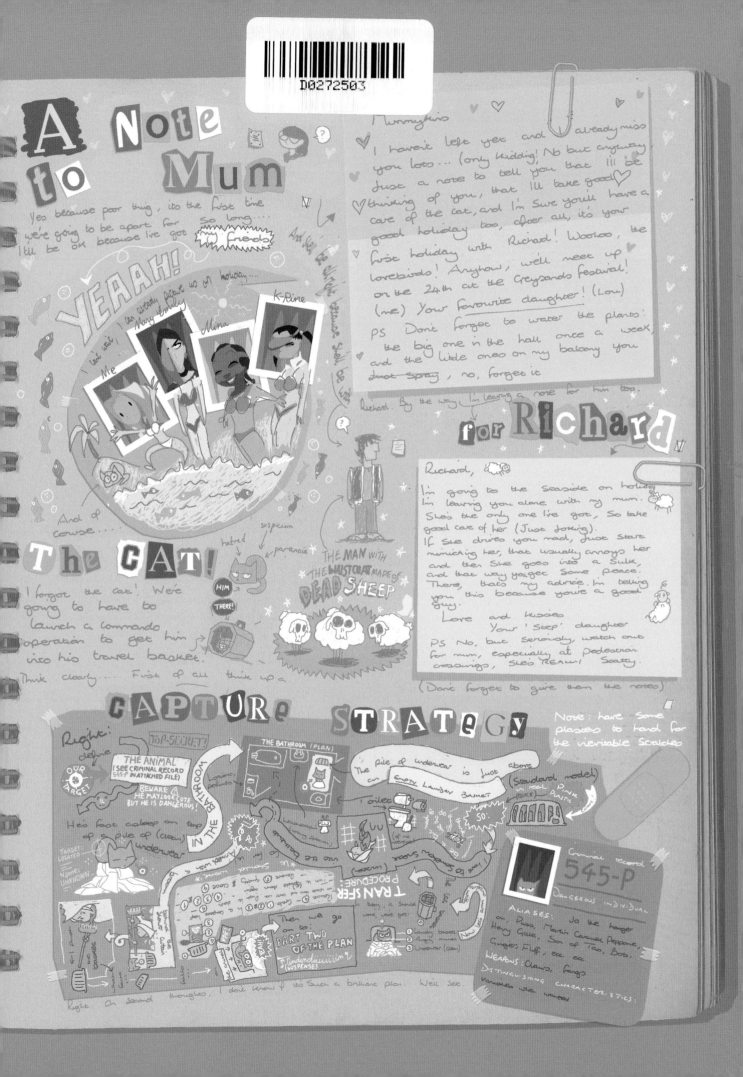

JULIEN NEEL

LOU! ④ ♥

ROMANCES

**ENGLISH TRANSLATION
BY ROS AND CHLOE SCHWARTZ**

USHARP
COMICS

First published in 2007
under the title *Idylles*
in the original French by
Editions Glénat
Couvent Sainte-Cécile
37, rue Servan - 38000 Grenoble

This English translation published
in 2011 by Usharp Comics,
an imprint of Highland Books Ltd
2 High Pines, Knoll Road
Godalming GU7 2EP
England.

English translation: © 2011 by Ros and Chloë Schwartz

Author's website: www.neelcartoons.com
ISBN-13: 978 1 905496 136
ISBN-10: 1-905496-13-3
Printed in Italy for Usharp L.E.G.O. S.p.A.

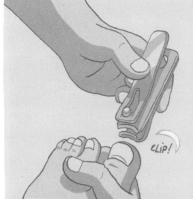

THIS IS THE FIRST SUMMER I'VE SPENT WITHOUT HER...

IT'S ALSO THE FIRST SUMMER YOU'VE SPENT WITH ME...

HAHAHA!

...AND D'YOU KNOW WHAT? WE MIGHT EVEN GET TO GO ON A ROMANTIC HOLIDAY TOGETHER, JUST THE TWO OF US!

WHAT?

MY PUBLISHER SENT ME MY SCHEDULE, AN AUTHOR TOUR WITH BOOK SIGNINGS UP AND DOWN THE COUNTRY...

... ALL EXPENSES PAID...

... POSH RESTAURANTS, LUXURY HOTELS ...

... JUST LIKE JAMES BOND

AND THE BEST BIT...

...IS THAT I CAN BRING MY SPOUSE

D'YOU MEAN ME?

YES, YOU TWIT!

WOO!

LIKE JAMES BOND, YOU SAID?

YUP!

WELL, WE MIGHT NOT HAVE A LICENCE TO KILL

I'LL ASK. YOU NEVER KNOW.

MWAH!

D'YOU THINK SHE'S MISSING ME JUST A TEENY LITTLE BIT?

4

5

6

7

14

18

21

27

29

30

36

37

39

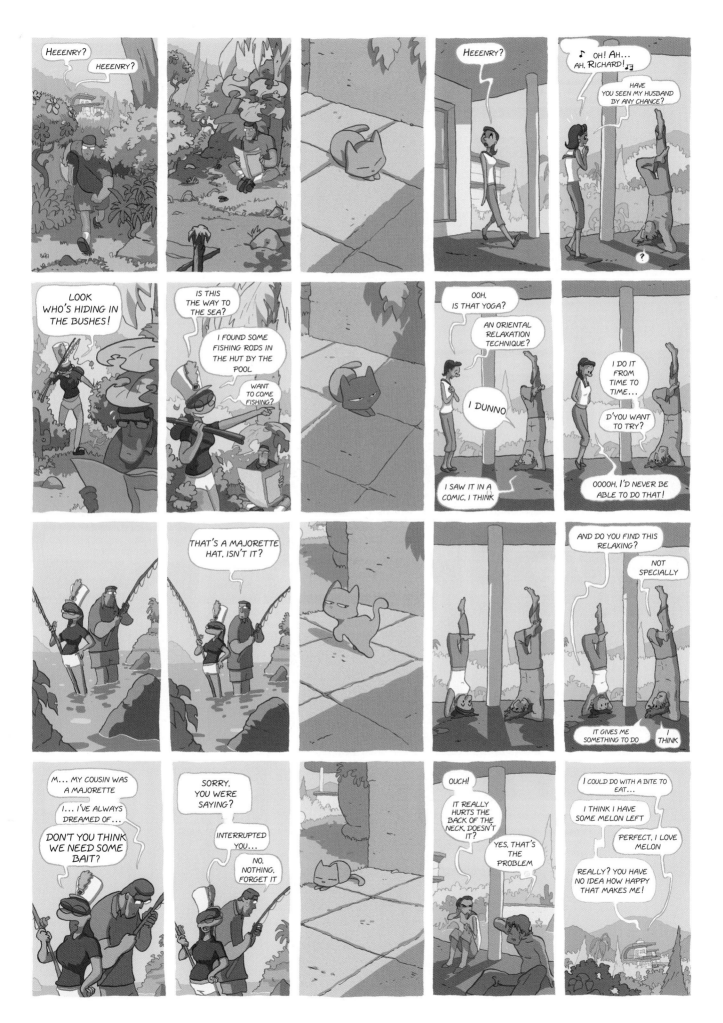

44